Let's Go!

written by Jesús Cervantes

photographs by Richard Hutchings

Scholastic Inc.
New York Toronto London Auckland Sydney
Mexico City New Delhi Hong Kong

Copyright © 2000 by Scholastic Inc.
SCHOLASTIC and associated logos and designs are
trademarks and/or registered trademarks of Scholastic Inc.
All rights reserved. Published by Scholastic Inc.
Printed in the U.S.A.
ISBN 0-439-14065-X

7 8 9 10   40   09

I go on a big bike.
Where will I go?

I go with my mom.
Where will I go?

I go in a car.

Where will I go?

I go in a cab.

Where will I go?

I go on the subway.

Where will I go?

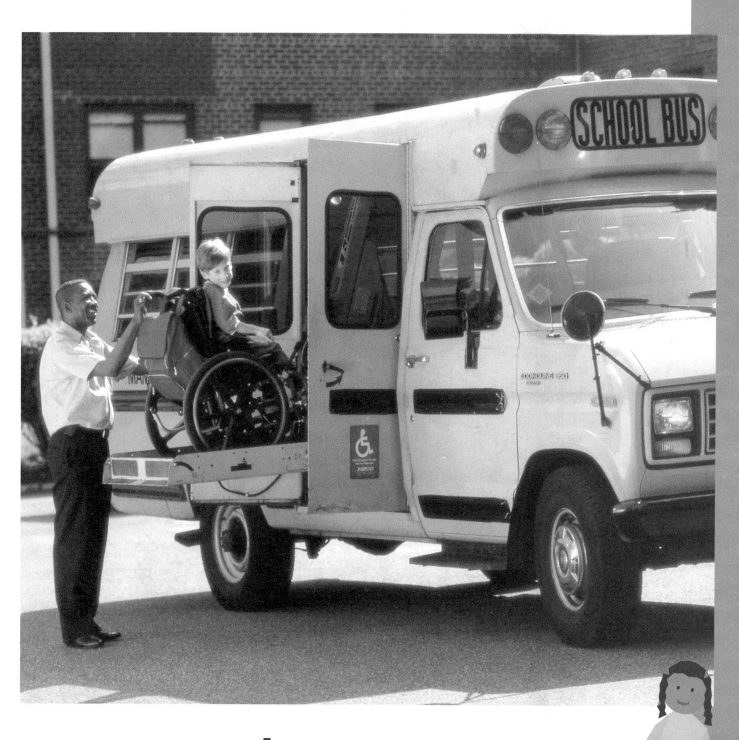

I go on a van.
Where will I go?

I go on a bus.
Where will I go?

To school!
We all go to school.

Chapter 2

We see our teacher at school.

Hello!

We sit on the mat and read.
We sit and write.

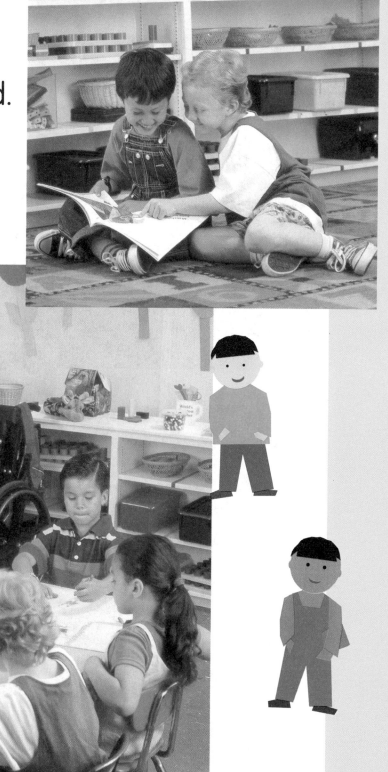

We play a lot.
We go up and down.

We sing.

We hop.

We paint.
We mop.

We read a lot.

Time to go.
Goodbye!